Old MacDonald had a Farm & other rhymes

Brown Watson
ENGLAND

First published 2016 by Brown Watson
The Old Mill, 76 Fleckney Road
Kibworth Beauchamp
Leicestershire LE8 0HG
ISBN: 978-0-7097-2318-9

Reprinted 2017
Printed in Malaysia

Old MacDonald had a Farm

Old MacDonald had a farm,
E-I-E-I-O!
And on that farm he had some chickens,
E-I-E-I-O!
With a cluck-cluck here,
And a cluck-cluck there
Here a cluck, there a cluck,
Everywhere a cluck-cluck
Old MacDonald had a farm
E-I-E-I-O!

Old MacDonald had a farm,
E-I-E-I-O!
And on that farm he had some cows,
E-I-E-I-O!
With a moo-moo here,
And a moo-moo there
Here a moo, there a moo,
Everywhere a moo-ooo
Old MacDonald had a farm,
E-I-E-I-O!

Old MacDonald had a farm,
E-I-E-I-O!
And on that farm he had some sheep
E-I-E-I-O!
With a baa-baa here,
And a baa-baa there
Here a baa, there a baa,
Everywhere a baa-baa
Old MacDonald had a farm,
E-I-E-I-O!

Old MacDonald had a farm,
E-I-E-I-O!
And on that farm he had some horses,
E-I-E-I-O!
With a neigh-neigh here,
And a neigh-neigh there
Here a neigh, there a neigh,
Everywhere a neigh-neigh
Old MacDonald had a farm,
E-I-E-I-O!

Sing a Song of Sixpence

Sing a song of sixpence, a pocket full of rye;
Four and twenty blackbirds baked in a pie.
When the pie was opened the birds began to sing,
Oh, wasn't that a dainty dish to set before the king!

The king was in his counting house, counting out his money;
The queen was in the parlour, eating bread and honey.
The maid was in the garden, hanging out the clothes;
When down came a blackbird and pecked off her nose!

Incy Wincy Spider

Incy Wincy Spider climbed up the water spout.
Down came the rain and washed the spider out.
Out came the sunshine and dried up all the rain,
And Incy Wincy Spider climbed up the spout again.

Ring-a-Ring O' Roses

Ring-a-ring o' roses,
A pocket full of posies,
A-tishoo! A-tishoo!
We all fall down.

The Wheels on the Bus

The wheels on the bus go round and round,
Round and round, round and round.
The wheels on the bus go round and round, all day long.

The horn on the bus goes beep, beep, beep,
Beep, beep, beep, beep, beep, beep.
The horn on the bus goes beep, beep, beep, all day long.

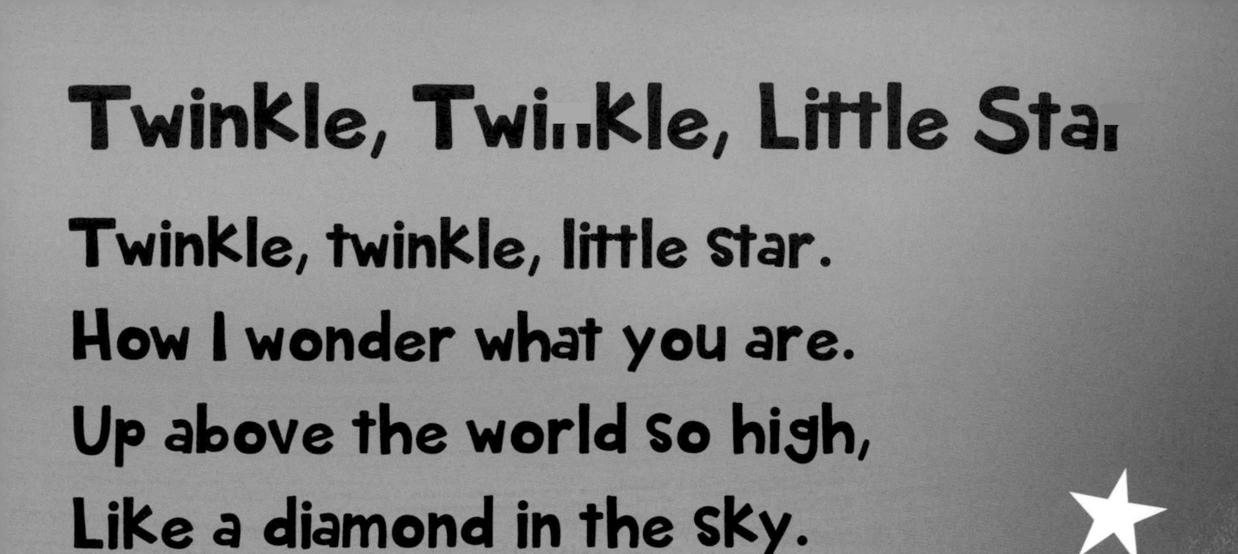

Twinkle, Twinkle, Little Star

Twinkle, twinkle, little star.
How I wonder what you are.
Up above the world so high,
Like a diamond in the sky.
Twinkle, twinkle, little star.
How I wonder what you are.

One, Two, Three, Four, Five

One, two, three, four, five,
Once I caught a fish alive,
Six, seven, eight, nine, ten,
Then I let it go again.
Why did you let it go?
Because it bit my finger so.
Which finger did it bite?
This little finger on my right.

Head, Shoulders, Knees and Toes

Head, shoulders, knees and toes, knees and toes,
Head, shoulders, knees and toes, knees and toes,

And eyes and ears and mouth and nose.
Head, shoulders, knees and toes, knees and toes.

It's Raining, It's Pouring

It's raining, it's pouring,
The old man is snoring.
He went to bed and bumped his head,
And he couldn't get up in the morning!

Oranges and Lemons

Oranges and lemons,
Say the bells of St. Clement's.
You owe me five farthings,
Say the bells of St. Martin's.
When will you pay me?
Say the bells of Old Bailey.
When I grow rich,
Say the bells of Shoreditch.
When will that be?
Say the bells of Stepney.
I do not know,
Says the great bell of Bow.
Here comes a candle to light you to bed,
And here comes a chopper to chop off your head!

Row, Row, Row Your Boat

Row, row, row your boat,
Gently down the stream.
Merrily, merrily, merrily, merrily
Life is but a dream.

Baa Baa Black Sheep

Baa baa black sheep, have you any wool?
Yes sir, yes sir, three bags full!
One for the master, one for the dame,
And one for the little boy
Who lives down the lane.

Polly Put the Kettle On

Polly put the kettle on,
Polly put the kettle on,
Polly put the kettle on,
We'll all have tea.
Sukey take it off again,
Sukey take it off again,
Sukey take it off again,
They've all gone away.

Here We Go Round the Mulberry Bush

Here we go round the mulberry bush,
The mulberry bush, the mulberry bush.
Here we go round the mulberry bush,
So early in the morning.

The Grand Old Duke of York

Oh, the Grand old Duke of York,
He had ten thousand men;
He marched them up to the top of the hill,
And he marched them down again.

When they were up, they were up,
And when they were down, they were down,
And when they were only halfway up,
They were neither up nor down.

Three blind mice, three blind mice,
See how they run, see how they run,
They all ran after the farmer's wife,
Who cut off their tails with a carving knife,
Did you ever see such a thing in your life,
As three blind mice?